THIS GLOW UP BELONGS TO:

_____

LOADING ...

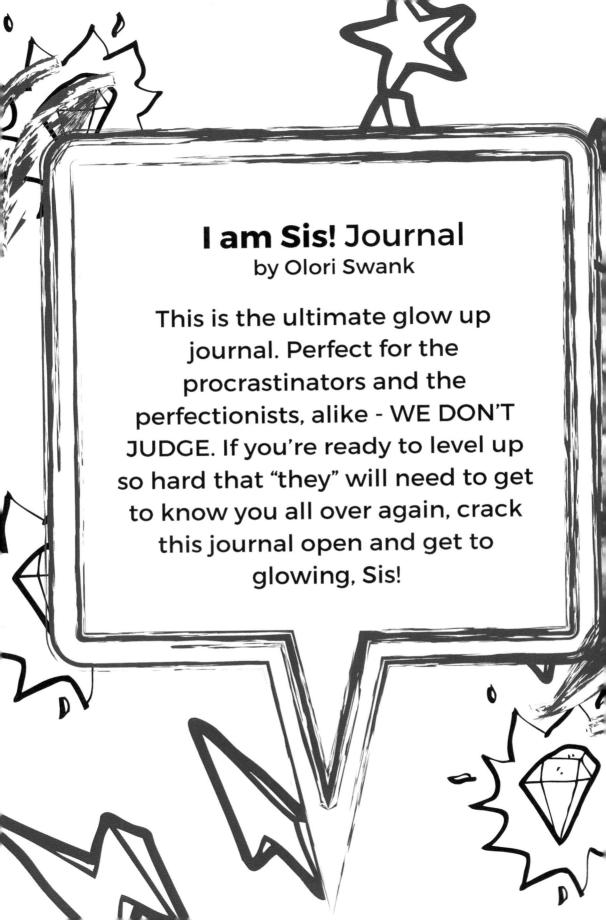

I am Sis! Journal
by Olori Swank

This is the ultimate glow up journal. Perfect for the procrastinators and the perfectionists, alike - WE DON'T JUDGE. If you're ready to level up so hard that "they" will need to get to know you all over again, crack this journal open and get to glowing, Sis!

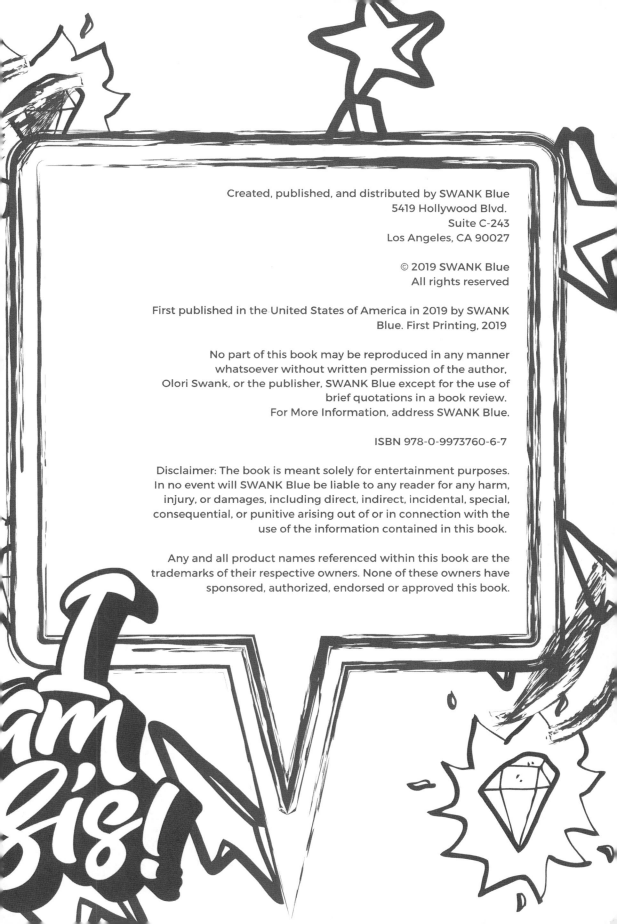

Created, published, and distributed by SWANK Blue
5419 Hollywood Blvd.
Suite C-243
Los Angeles, CA 90027

First published in the United States of America in 2019 by SWANK Blue. First Printing, 2019

ISBN 978-0-9973760-6-7

Disclaimer: The book is meant solely for entertainment purposes. In no event will SWANK Blue be liable to any reader for any harm, injury, or damages, including direct, indirect, incidental, special, consequential, or punitive arising out of or in connection with the use of the information contained in this book.

Any and all product names referenced within this book are the trademarks of their respective owners. None of these owners have sponsored, authorized, endorsed or approved this book.

HOW I'M LEVELING UP TODAY

_____

_____

_____

_____

_____

_____

_____

_____

_____

_____

_____

_____

_____

_____

_____

_____

_____

_____

_____

_____

MY LEVEL OF CONFIDENCE TODAY:

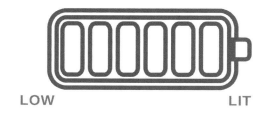

LOW   LIT

TODAY'S DATE: _____

HOW I'M LEVELING UP TODAY

_____
_____
_____
_____
_____
_____
_____
_____
_____
_____
_____
_____
_____
_____
_____
_____
_____
_____
_____

MY LEVEL OF CONFIDENCE TODAY:

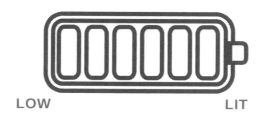

LOW   LIT

TODAY'S DATE: _____

HOW I'M LEVELING UP TODAY

_____

_____

_____

_____

_____

_____

_____

_____

_____

_____

_____

_____

_____

_____

_____

_____

_____

_____

_____

MY LEVEL OF CONFIDENCE TODAY:

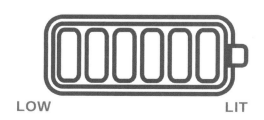

LOW   LIT

TODAY'S DATE: _____

HOW I'M LEVELING UP TODAY

_____
_____
_____
_____
_____
_____
_____
_____
_____
_____
_____
_____
_____
_____
_____
_____
_____
_____
_____
_____

MY LEVEL OF CONFIDENCE TODAY:

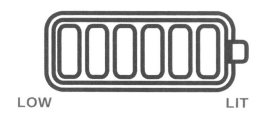

LOW   LIT

TODAY'S DATE: _____

HOW I'M LEVELING UP TODAY

_____
_____
_____
_____
_____
_____
_____
_____
_____
_____
_____
_____
_____
_____
_____
_____
_____
_____
_____
_____

MY LEVEL OF CONFIDENCE TODAY:

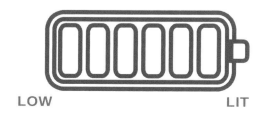

LOW   LIT

TODAY'S DATE: _____

HOW I'M LEVELING UP TODAY

_____

_____

_____

_____

_____

_____

_____

_____

_____

_____

_____

_____

_____

_____

_____

_____

_____

MY LEVEL OF CONFIDENCE TODAY:

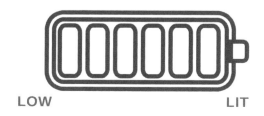

LOW   LIT

TODAY'S DATE: _____

HOW I'M LEVELING UP TODAY

_____
_____
_____
_____
_____
_____
_____
_____
_____
_____
_____
_____
_____
_____
_____
_____
_____
_____
_____
_____
_____
_____
_____

MY LEVEL OF CONFIDENCE TODAY:

LOW   LIT

TODAY'S DATE: _____

HOW I'M LEVELING UP TODAY

_____

_____

_____

_____

_____

_____

_____

_____

_____

_____

_____

_____

_____

_____

_____

_____

_____

_____

MY LEVEL OF CONFIDENCE TODAY:

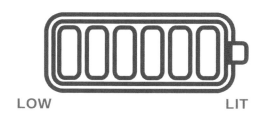

LOW   LIT

TODAY'S DATE: _____

HOW I'M LEVELING UP TODAY

_____

_____

_____

_____

_____

_____

_____

_____

_____

_____

_____

_____

_____

_____

_____

_____

_____

MY LEVEL OF CONFIDENCE TODAY:

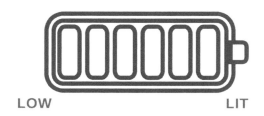

LOW   LIT

TODAY'S DATE: _____

HOW I'M LEVELING UP TODAY

_____

_____

_____

_____

_____

_____

_____

_____

_____

_____

_____

_____

_____

_____

_____

_____

_____

_____

_____

_____

_____

MY LEVEL OF CONFIDENCE TODAY:

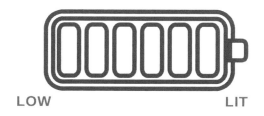

LOW   LIT

TODAY'S DATE: _____

HOW I'M LEVELING UP TODAY

_____

_____

_____

_____

_____

_____

_____

_____

_____

_____

_____

_____

_____

_____

_____

_____

_____

_____

_____

MY LEVEL OF CONFIDENCE TODAY:

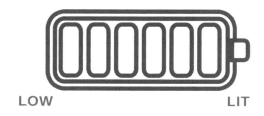

LOW   LIT

Olori SWANK ✔
@OloriSWANK

If you truly love someone, take some time to learn how to love them in their own love language (NOT yours). I've seen too many people try to force their personal love language onto their partner then get frustrated when their partner doesn't feel loved.

HOW I'M LEVELING UP TODAY

_____

_____

_____

_____

_____

_____

_____

_____

_____

_____

_____

_____

_____

_____

_____

_____

_____

_____

_____

_____

MY LEVEL OF CONFIDENCE TODAY:

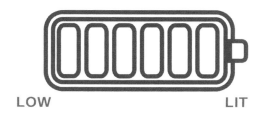

LOW   LIT

TODAY'S DATE: _____

HOW I'M LEVELING UP TODAY

MY LEVEL OF CONFIDENCE TODAY:

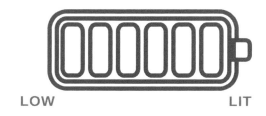

LOW   LIT

TODAY'S DATE: _____

HOW I'M LEVELING UP TODAY

_____

_____

_____

_____

_____

_____

_____

_____

_____

_____

_____

_____

_____

_____

_____

_____

_____

_____

_____

_____

_____

MY LEVEL OF CONFIDENCE TODAY:

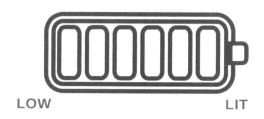

LOW   LIT

TODAY'S DATE: _____

HOW I'M LEVELING UP TODAY

_____

_____

_____

_____

_____

_____

_____

_____

_____

_____

_____

_____

_____

_____

_____

_____

_____

_____

_____

MY LEVEL OF CONFIDENCE TODAY:

LOW   LIT

TODAY'S DATE: _____

HOW I'M LEVELING UP TODAY

_____

_____

_____

_____

_____

_____

_____

_____

_____

_____

_____

_____

_____

_____

_____

_____

_____

_____

_____

_____

MY LEVEL OF CONFIDENCE TODAY:

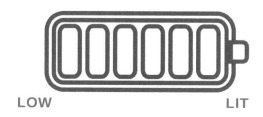

LOW   LIT

TODAY'S DATE: _____

HOW I'M LEVELING UP TODAY

_____

_____

_____

_____

_____

_____

_____

_____

_____

_____

_____

_____

_____

_____

_____

_____

_____

MY LEVEL OF CONFIDENCE TODAY:

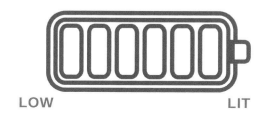

LOW   LIT

TODAY'S DATE: _____

HOW I'M LEVELING UP TODAY

_____

_____

_____

_____

_____

_____

_____

_____

_____

_____

_____

_____

_____

_____

_____

_____

_____

_____

_____

MY LEVEL OF CONFIDENCE TODAY:

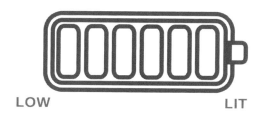

LOW   LIT

TODAY'S DATE: _____

HOW I'M LEVELING UP TODAY

MY LEVEL OF CONFIDENCE TODAY:

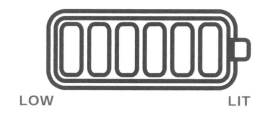

LOW   LIT

TODAY'S DATE: _____

HOW I'M LEVELING UP TODAY

_____
_____
_____
_____
_____
_____
_____
_____
_____
_____
_____
_____
_____
_____
_____
_____
_____
_____
_____
_____

MY LEVEL OF CONFIDENCE TODAY:

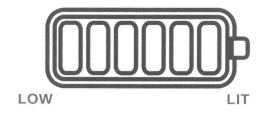

LOW   LIT

TODAY'S DATE: _____

HOW I'M LEVELING UP TODAY

_____

_____

_____

_____

_____

_____

_____

_____

_____

_____

_____

_____

_____

_____

_____

_____

_____

_____

_____

_____

MY LEVEL OF CONFIDENCE TODAY:

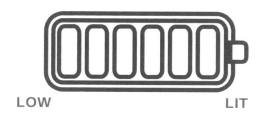

LOW   LIT

TODAY'S DATE: _____

HOW I'M LEVELING UP TODAY

_____
_____
_____
_____
_____
_____
_____
_____
_____
_____
_____
_____
_____
_____
_____
_____
_____
_____
_____

MY LEVEL OF CONFIDENCE TODAY:

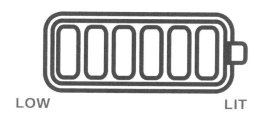

LOW   LIT

TODAY'S DATE: _____

HOW I'M LEVELING UP TODAY

_____

_____

_____

_____

_____

_____

_____

_____

_____

_____

_____

_____

_____

_____

_____

_____

MY LEVEL OF CONFIDENCE TODAY:

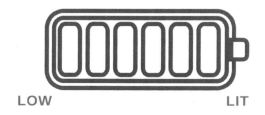

LOW   LIT

TODAY'S DATE: _____

HOW I'M LEVELING UP TODAY

_____

_____

_____

_____

_____

_____

_____

_____

_____

_____

_____

_____

_____

_____

_____

_____

_____

_____

_____

_____

_____

MY LEVEL OF CONFIDENCE TODAY:

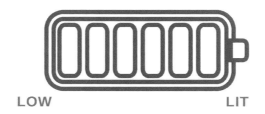

LOW   LIT

HOW I'M LEVELING UP TODAY

_____
_____
_____
_____
_____
_____
_____
_____
_____
_____
_____
_____
_____
_____
_____
_____
_____

MY LEVEL OF CONFIDENCE TODAY:

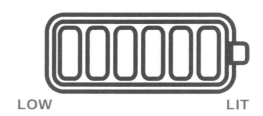

LOW   LIT

HOW I'M LEVELING UP TODAY

_____

_____

_____

_____

_____

_____

_____

_____

_____

_____

_____

_____

_____

_____

_____

_____

_____

_____

_____

MY LEVEL OF CONFIDENCE TODAY:

LOW   LIT

TODAY'S DATE: _____

HOW I'M LEVELING UP TODAY

_____

_____

_____

_____

_____

_____

_____

_____

_____

_____

_____

_____

_____

_____

_____

_____

_____

MY LEVEL OF CONFIDENCE TODAY:

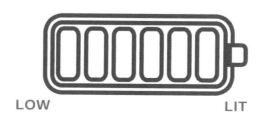

LOW   LIT

TODAY'S DATE: _____

HOW I'M LEVELING UP TODAY

_____
_____
_____
_____
_____
_____
_____
_____
_____
_____
_____
_____
_____
_____
_____
_____
_____
_____
_____
_____
_____

MY LEVEL OF CONFIDENCE TODAY:

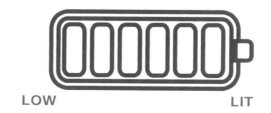

LOW   LIT

HOW I'M LEVELING UP TODAY

_____
_____
_____
_____
_____
_____
_____
_____
_____
_____
_____
_____
_____
_____
_____
_____
_____

MY LEVEL OF CONFIDENCE TODAY:

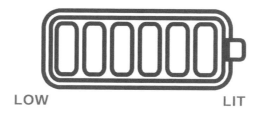

LOW   LIT

TODAY'S DATE: _____

HOW I'M LEVELING UP TODAY

_____

_____

_____

_____

_____

_____

_____

_____

_____

_____

_____

_____

_____

_____

_____

_____

_____

_____

_____

_____

MY LEVEL OF CONFIDENCE TODAY:

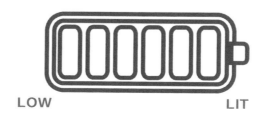

LOW   LIT

HOW I'M LEVELING UP TODAY

_____

_____

_____

_____

_____

_____

_____

_____

_____

_____

_____

_____

_____

_____

_____

_____

_____

_____

_____

_____

MY LEVEL OF CONFIDENCE TODAY:

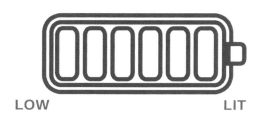

LOW   LIT

TODAY'S DATE: _____

HOW I'M LEVELING UP TODAY

_____
_____
_____
_____
_____
_____
_____
_____
_____
_____
_____
_____
_____
_____
_____
_____
_____
_____
_____
_____

MY LEVEL OF CONFIDENCE TODAY:

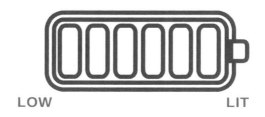

LOW   LIT

TODAY'S DATE: _____

HOW I'M LEVELING UP TODAY

_____
_____
_____
_____
_____
_____
_____
_____
_____
_____
_____
_____
_____
_____
_____
_____
_____
_____

MY LEVEL OF CONFIDENCE TODAY:

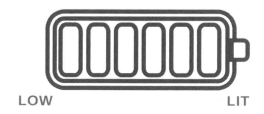

LOW   LIT

TODAY'S DATE: _____

HOW I'M LEVELING UP TODAY

_____
_____
_____
_____
_____
_____
_____
_____
_____
_____
_____
_____
_____
_____
_____
_____
_____
_____
_____

MY LEVEL OF CONFIDENCE TODAY:

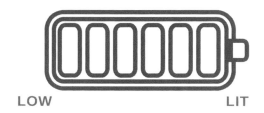

LOW   LIT

TODAY'S DATE: _____

HOW I'M LEVELING UP TODAY

_____

_____

_____

_____

_____

_____

_____

_____

_____

_____

_____

_____

_____

_____

_____

_____

_____

_____

_____

_____

MY LEVEL OF CONFIDENCE TODAY:

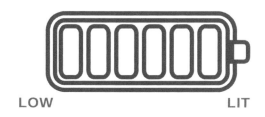

LOW   LIT

TODAY'S DATE: _____

HOW I'M LEVELING UP TODAY

_____
_____
_____
_____
_____
_____
_____
_____
_____
_____
_____
_____
_____
_____
_____
_____
_____
_____

MY LEVEL OF CONFIDENCE TODAY:

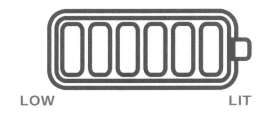

LOW   LIT

TODAY'S DATE: _____

HOW I'M LEVELING UP TODAY

MY LEVEL OF CONFIDENCE TODAY:

LOW   LIT

TODAY'S DATE: _____

HOW I'M LEVELING UP TODAY

_____
_____
_____
_____
_____
_____
_____
_____
_____
_____
_____
_____
_____
_____
_____
_____
_____
_____

MY LEVEL OF CONFIDENCE TODAY:

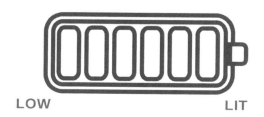

LOW   LIT

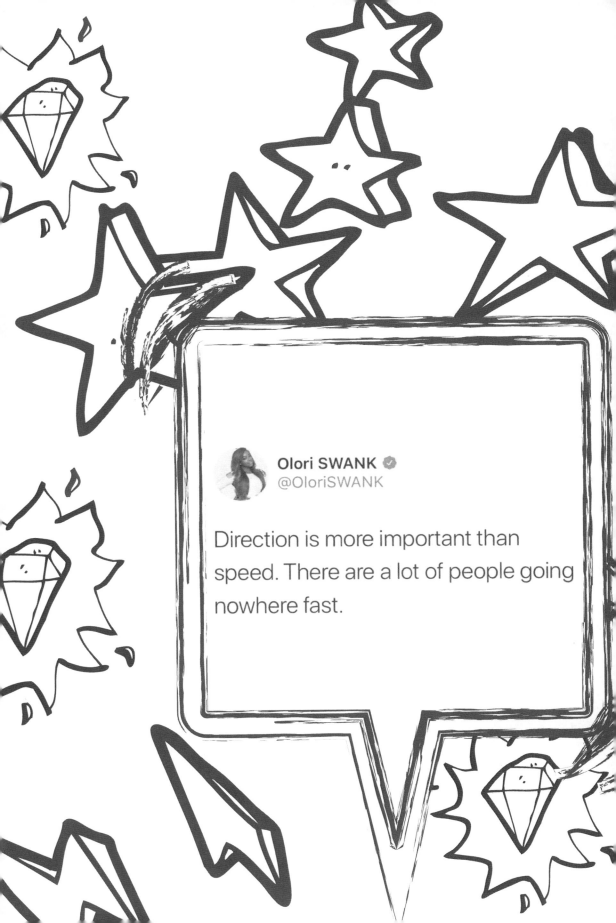

TODAY'S DATE: _____

HOW I'M LEVELING UP TODAY

_____

_____

_____

_____

_____

_____

_____

_____

_____

_____

_____

_____

_____

_____

_____

_____

_____

_____

_____

_____

_____

_____

MY LEVEL OF CONFIDENCE TODAY:

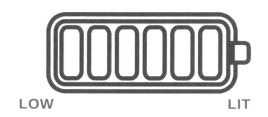

LOW   LIT

TODAY'S DATE: _____

HOW I'M LEVELING UP TODAY

_____

_____

_____

_____

_____

_____

_____

_____

_____

_____

_____

_____

_____

_____

_____

_____

_____

_____

_____

_____

_____

MY LEVEL OF CONFIDENCE TODAY:

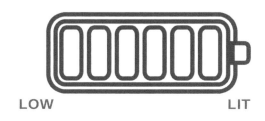

LOW   LIT

TODAY'S DATE: _____

HOW I'M LEVELING UP TODAY

_____
_____
_____
_____
_____
_____
_____
_____
_____
_____
_____
_____
_____
_____
_____
_____
_____
_____

MY LEVEL OF CONFIDENCE TODAY:

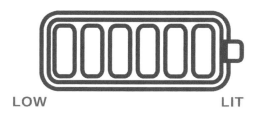

LOW   LIT

TODAY'S DATE: _____

HOW I'M LEVELING UP TODAY

_____

_____

_____

_____

_____

_____

_____

_____

_____

_____

_____

_____

_____

_____

_____

_____

_____

_____

_____

_____

MY LEVEL OF CONFIDENCE TODAY:

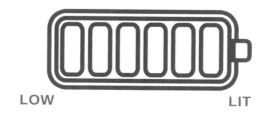

LOW   LIT

TODAY'S DATE: _____

HOW I'M LEVELING UP TODAY

_____

_____

_____

_____

_____

_____

_____

_____

_____

_____

_____

_____

_____

_____

_____

_____

_____

_____

_____

MY LEVEL OF CONFIDENCE TODAY:

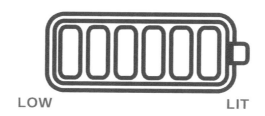

LOW   LIT

TODAY'S DATE: _____

HOW I'M LEVELING UP TODAY

_____
_____
_____
_____
_____
_____
_____
_____
_____
_____
_____
_____
_____
_____
_____
_____
_____
_____
_____
_____

MY LEVEL OF CONFIDENCE TODAY:

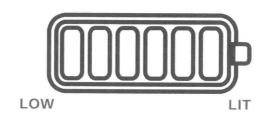

LOW   LIT

TODAY'S DATE: _____

HOW I'M LEVELING UP TODAY

_____

_____

_____

_____

_____

_____

_____

_____

_____

_____

_____

_____

_____

_____

_____

_____

_____

_____

MY LEVEL OF CONFIDENCE TODAY:

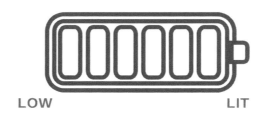

LOW   LIT

TODAY'S DATE: _____

HOW I'M LEVELING UP TODAY

_____

_____

_____

_____

_____

_____

_____

_____

_____

_____

_____

_____

_____

_____

_____

_____

_____

_____

MY LEVEL OF CONFIDENCE TODAY:

LOW   LIT

TODAY'S DATE: _____

HOW I'M LEVELING UP TODAY

_____
_____
_____
_____
_____
_____
_____
_____
_____
_____
_____
_____
_____
_____
_____
_____
_____
_____
_____

MY LEVEL OF CONFIDENCE TODAY:

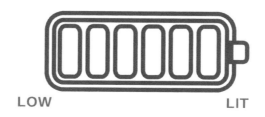

LOW   LIT

TODAY'S DATE: _____

HOW I'M LEVELING UP TODAY

_____

_____

_____

_____

_____

_____

_____

_____

_____

_____

_____

_____

_____

_____

_____

_____

_____

_____

MY LEVEL OF CONFIDENCE TODAY:

LOW   LIT

TODAY'S DATE: _____

HOW I'M LEVELING UP TODAY

_____

_____

_____

_____

_____

_____

_____

_____

_____

_____

_____

_____

_____

_____

_____

_____

_____

MY LEVEL OF CONFIDENCE TODAY:

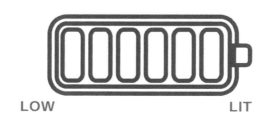

LOW   LIT

TODAY'S DATE: _____

HOW I'M LEVELING UP TODAY

_____

_____

_____

_____

_____

_____

_____

_____

_____

_____

_____

_____

_____

_____

_____

_____

MY LEVEL OF CONFIDENCE TODAY:

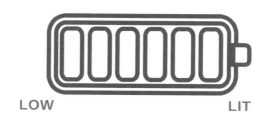

LOW   LIT

Olori SWANK ✓
@OloriSWANK

Your life is about breaking your own limits and outgrowing yourself. Stop worrying about what others are achieving; and stop trying to compete with others. It's time to outdo your past. It's time to stunt on yourself. It's time to put your foot on your own neck.

TODAY'S DATE: _____

HOW I'M LEVELING UP TODAY

_____
_____
_____
_____
_____
_____
_____
_____
_____
_____
_____
_____
_____
_____
_____
_____
_____
_____
_____
_____

MY LEVEL OF CONFIDENCE TODAY:

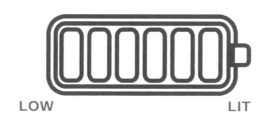

LOW   LIT

TODAY'S DATE: _____

HOW I'M LEVELING UP TODAY

_____
_____
_____
_____
_____
_____
_____
_____
_____
_____
_____
_____
_____
_____
_____
_____
_____
_____
_____

MY LEVEL OF CONFIDENCE TODAY:

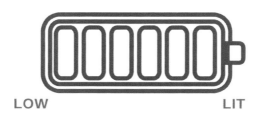

LOW   LIT

TODAY'S DATE: _____

HOW I'M LEVELING UP TODAY

_____
_____
_____
_____
_____
_____
_____
_____
_____
_____
_____
_____
_____
_____
_____
_____
_____
_____
_____

MY LEVEL OF CONFIDENCE TODAY:

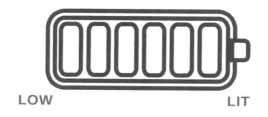

LOW   LIT

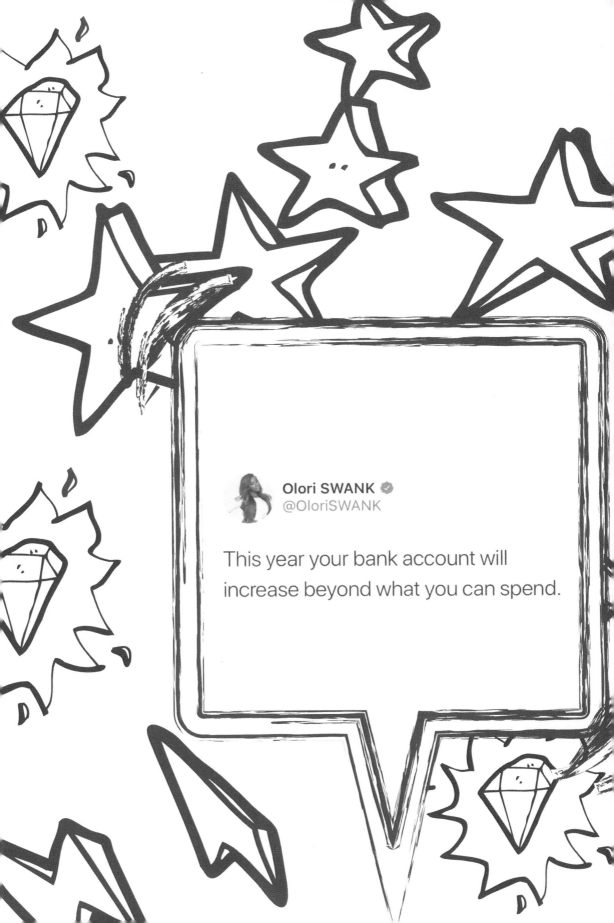

TODAY'S DATE: _____

HOW I'M LEVELING UP TODAY

MY LEVEL OF CONFIDENCE TODAY:

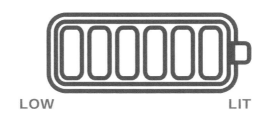

LOW   LIT

TODAY'S DATE: _____

HOW I'M LEVELING UP TODAY

_____

_____

_____

_____

_____

_____

_____

_____

_____

_____

_____

_____

_____

_____

_____

_____

_____

_____

MY LEVEL OF CONFIDENCE TODAY:

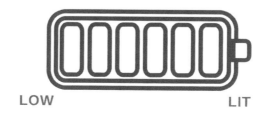

LOW   LIT

TODAY'S DATE: _____

HOW I'M LEVELING UP TODAY

_____

_____

_____

_____

_____

_____

_____

_____

_____

_____

_____

_____

_____

_____

_____

_____

_____

_____

MY LEVEL OF CONFIDENCE TODAY:

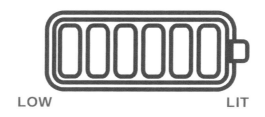

LOW   LIT

Olori SWANK ✔
@OloriSWANK

Discipline will carry you on the days motivation fails you.

TODAY'S DATE: _____

HOW I'M LEVELING UP TODAY

_____
_____
_____
_____
_____
_____
_____
_____
_____
_____
_____
_____
_____
_____
_____
_____
_____
_____
_____

MY LEVEL OF CONFIDENCE TODAY:

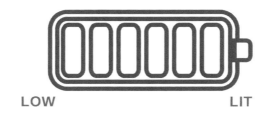

LOW   LIT

TODAY'S DATE: _____

HOW I'M LEVELING UP TODAY

_____
_____
_____
_____
_____
_____
_____
_____
_____
_____
_____
_____
_____
_____
_____
_____
_____
_____
_____
_____

MY LEVEL OF CONFIDENCE TODAY:

LOW   LIT

TODAY'S DATE: _____

HOW I'M LEVELING UP TODAY

_____

_____

_____

_____

_____

_____

_____

_____

_____

_____

_____

_____

_____

_____

_____

_____

_____

_____

_____

MY LEVEL OF CONFIDENCE TODAY:

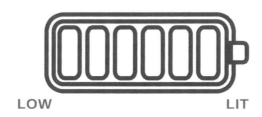

LOW   LIT

TODAY'S DATE: _____

HOW I'M LEVELING UP TODAY

_____

_____

_____

_____

_____

_____

_____

_____

_____

_____

_____

_____

_____

_____

_____

_____

_____

MY LEVEL OF CONFIDENCE TODAY:

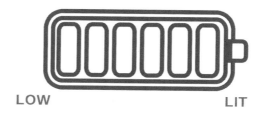

LOW   LIT

TODAY'S DATE: _____

HOW I'M LEVELING UP TODAY

_____
_____
_____
_____
_____
_____
_____
_____
_____
_____
_____
_____
_____
_____
_____
_____
_____
_____

MY LEVEL OF CONFIDENCE TODAY:

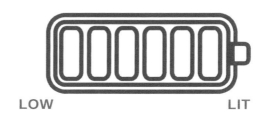

LOW   LIT

TODAY'S DATE: _____

HOW I'M LEVELING UP TODAY

_____

_____

_____

_____

_____

_____

_____

_____

_____

_____

_____

_____

_____

_____

_____

_____

_____

_____

MY LEVEL OF CONFIDENCE TODAY:

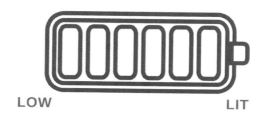

LOW   LIT

TODAY'S DATE: _____

HOW I'M LEVELING UP TODAY

_____
_____
_____
_____
_____
_____
_____
_____
_____
_____
_____
_____
_____
_____
_____
_____
_____
_____
_____
_____
_____

MY LEVEL OF CONFIDENCE TODAY:

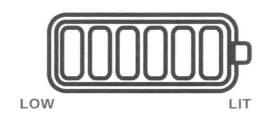

LOW   LIT

Olori SWANK ✓
@OloriSWANK

You're not always going to be motivated. So learning how to be disciplined is incredibly important.

TODAY'S DATE: _____

HOW I'M LEVELING UP TODAY

_____
_____
_____
_____
_____
_____
_____
_____
_____
_____
_____
_____
_____
_____
_____
_____
_____
_____

MY LEVEL OF CONFIDENCE TODAY:

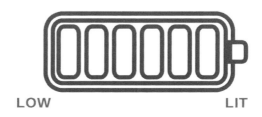

LOW   LIT

TODAY'S DATE: _____

HOW I'M LEVELING UP TODAY

_____

_____

_____

_____

_____

_____

_____

_____

_____

_____

_____

_____

_____

_____

_____

_____

MY LEVEL OF CONFIDENCE TODAY:

LOW   LIT

TODAY'S DATE: _____

HOW I'M LEVELING UP TODAY

_____

_____

_____

_____

_____

_____

_____

_____

_____

_____

_____

_____

_____

_____

_____

_____

_____

_____

MY LEVEL OF CONFIDENCE TODAY:

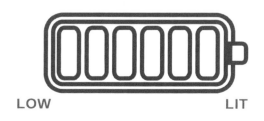

LOW   LIT

Olori SWANK ✔
@OloriSWANK

You don't have to be the same person you used to be. You can completely recreate yourself. Learn new things; think new thoughts; make better choices; create new habits. All you have to do is create an image of the greatest version of yourself, and make the commitment to be that.

TODAY'S DATE: _____

HOW I'M LEVELING UP TODAY

_____
_____
_____
_____
_____
_____
_____
_____
_____
_____
_____
_____
_____
_____
_____
_____
_____
_____
_____
_____
_____

MY LEVEL OF CONFIDENCE TODAY:

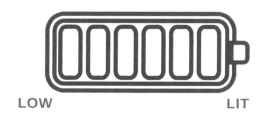

LOW   LIT

TODAY'S DATE: _____

HOW I'M LEVELING UP TODAY

_____
_____
_____
_____
_____
_____
_____
_____
_____
_____
_____
_____
_____
_____
_____
_____
_____
_____
_____
_____

MY LEVEL OF CONFIDENCE TODAY:

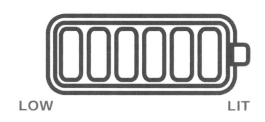

LOW   LIT

TODAY'S DATE: _____

HOW I'M LEVELING UP TODAY

_____

_____

_____

_____

_____

_____

_____

_____

_____

_____

_____

_____

_____

_____

_____

_____

_____

MY LEVEL OF CONFIDENCE TODAY:

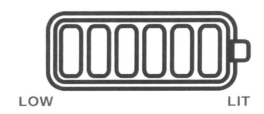

LOW   LIT

TODAY'S DATE: _____

HOW I'M LEVELING UP TODAY

_____
_____
_____
_____
_____
_____
_____
_____
_____
_____
_____
_____
_____
_____
_____
_____
_____
_____
_____
_____
_____

MY LEVEL OF CONFIDENCE TODAY:

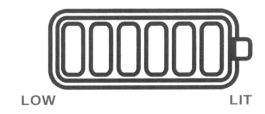

LOW   LIT

Olori SWANK ✔
@OloriSWANK

Goal: To make an income while making an impact.

TODAY'S DATE: _____

HOW I'M LEVELING UP TODAY

_____
_____
_____
_____
_____
_____
_____
_____
_____
_____
_____
_____
_____
_____
_____
_____
_____
_____
_____
_____
_____

MY LEVEL OF CONFIDENCE TODAY:

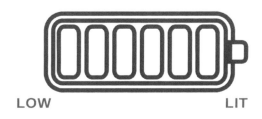

LOW   LIT

TODAY'S DATE: _____

HOW I'M LEVELING UP TODAY

_____
_____
_____
_____
_____
_____
_____
_____
_____
_____
_____
_____
_____
_____
_____
_____
_____
_____
_____

MY LEVEL OF CONFIDENCE TODAY:

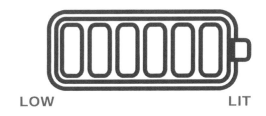

LOW   LIT

TODAY'S DATE: _____

HOW I'M LEVELING UP TODAY

_____
_____
_____
_____
_____
_____
_____
_____
_____
_____
_____
_____
_____
_____
_____
_____
_____
_____

MY LEVEL OF CONFIDENCE TODAY:

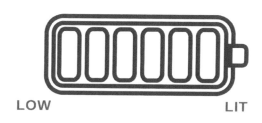

LOW   LIT

TODAY'S DATE: _____

HOW I'M LEVELING UP TODAY

_____
_____
_____
_____
_____
_____
_____
_____
_____
_____
_____
_____
_____
_____
_____
_____
_____
_____
_____
_____

MY LEVEL OF CONFIDENCE TODAY:

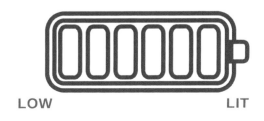

LOW   LIT

TODAY'S DATE: _____

HOW I'M LEVELING UP TODAY

_____

_____

_____

_____

_____

_____

_____

_____

_____

_____

_____

_____

_____

_____

_____

_____

_____

_____

_____

_____

_____

_____

_____

MY LEVEL OF CONFIDENCE TODAY:

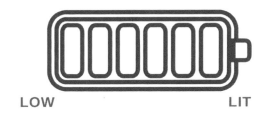

LOW   LIT

TODAY'S DATE: _____

HOW I'M LEVELING UP TODAY

_____
_____
_____
_____
_____
_____
_____
_____
_____
_____
_____
_____
_____
_____
_____
_____
_____
_____
_____
_____

MY LEVEL OF CONFIDENCE TODAY:

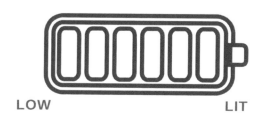

LOW   LIT

Olori SWANK ✓
@OloriSWANK

I started making so much more progress in life when I stopped trying to calm the storm and I calmed myself instead. Storms pass. ...It's not about avoiding them; it's about surviving them.

TODAY'S DATE: _____

HOW I'M LEVELING UP TODAY

_____
_____
_____
_____
_____
_____
_____
_____
_____
_____
_____
_____
_____
_____
_____
_____
_____
_____

MY LEVEL OF CONFIDENCE TODAY:

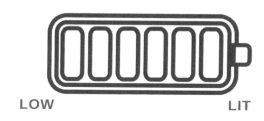

LOW   LIT

TODAY'S DATE: _____

HOW I'M LEVELING UP TODAY

_____
_____
_____
_____
_____
_____
_____
_____
_____
_____
_____
_____
_____
_____
_____
_____
_____
_____
_____

MY LEVEL OF CONFIDENCE TODAY:

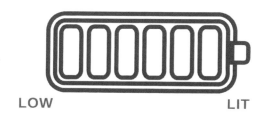

LOW   LIT

TODAY'S DATE: _____

HOW I'M LEVELING UP TODAY

_____
_____
_____
_____
_____
_____
_____
_____
_____
_____
_____
_____
_____
_____
_____
_____
_____
_____
_____
_____
_____

MY LEVEL OF CONFIDENCE TODAY:

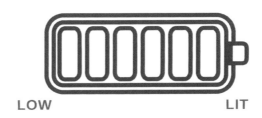

LOW   LIT

TODAY'S DATE: _____

HOW I'M LEVELING UP TODAY

_____

_____

_____

_____

_____

_____

_____

_____

_____

_____

_____

_____

_____

_____

_____

_____

_____

_____

_____

_____

_____

MY LEVEL OF CONFIDENCE TODAY:

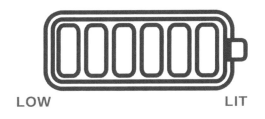

LOW   LIT

TODAY'S DATE: _____

HOW I'M LEVELING UP TODAY

_____
_____
_____
_____
_____
_____
_____
_____
_____
_____
_____
_____
_____
_____
_____
_____
_____
_____
_____
_____
_____
_____
_____

MY LEVEL OF CONFIDENCE TODAY:

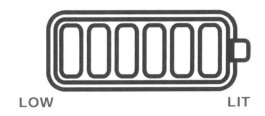

LOW   LIT

TODAY'S DATE: _____

HOW I'M LEVELING UP TODAY

_____
_____
_____
_____
_____
_____
_____
_____
_____
_____
_____
_____
_____
_____
_____
_____
_____
_____
_____
_____
_____

MY LEVEL OF CONFIDENCE TODAY:

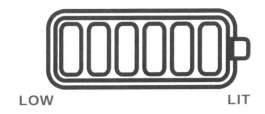

LOW   LIT

Olori SWANK ✔
@OloriSWANK

Failure is a part of learning. If you fear failure, you fear growth.

TODAY'S DATE: _____

HOW I'M LEVELING UP TODAY

_____
_____
_____
_____
_____
_____
_____
_____
_____
_____
_____
_____
_____
_____
_____
_____
_____
_____
_____
_____

MY LEVEL OF CONFIDENCE TODAY:

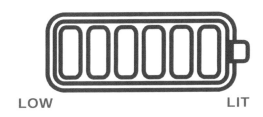

LOW   LIT

TODAY'S DATE: _____

HOW I'M LEVELING UP TODAY

_____
_____
_____
_____
_____
_____
_____
_____
_____
_____
_____
_____
_____
_____
_____
_____
_____
_____

MY LEVEL OF CONFIDENCE TODAY:

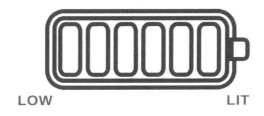

LOW   LIT

Olori SWANK ✓
@OloriSWANK

You've got to be willing to go after it without support. The sad truth is that the ones you except to support your endeavors; might turn out to be the last ones to. You can't let lack of "support" stop you from chasing your dreams.

TODAY'S DATE: _____

HOW I'M LEVELING UP TODAY

_____
_____
_____
_____
_____
_____
_____
_____
_____
_____
_____
_____
_____
_____
_____
_____
_____
_____
_____
_____

MY LEVEL OF CONFIDENCE TODAY:

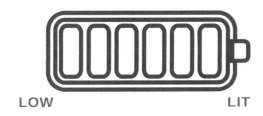

LOW   LIT